Rowing Down the River

By Becky Wiinikainen

Illustrated by Kelly Nogoski

First published by Experience Early Learning Company
7243 Scotchwood Lane, Grawn, Michigan 49637 USA

Text Copyright ©2016 by Experience Early Learning Co.
Printed and Bound in the USA

ISBN 978-1-937954-32-1
visit us at www.ExperienceEarlyLearning.com

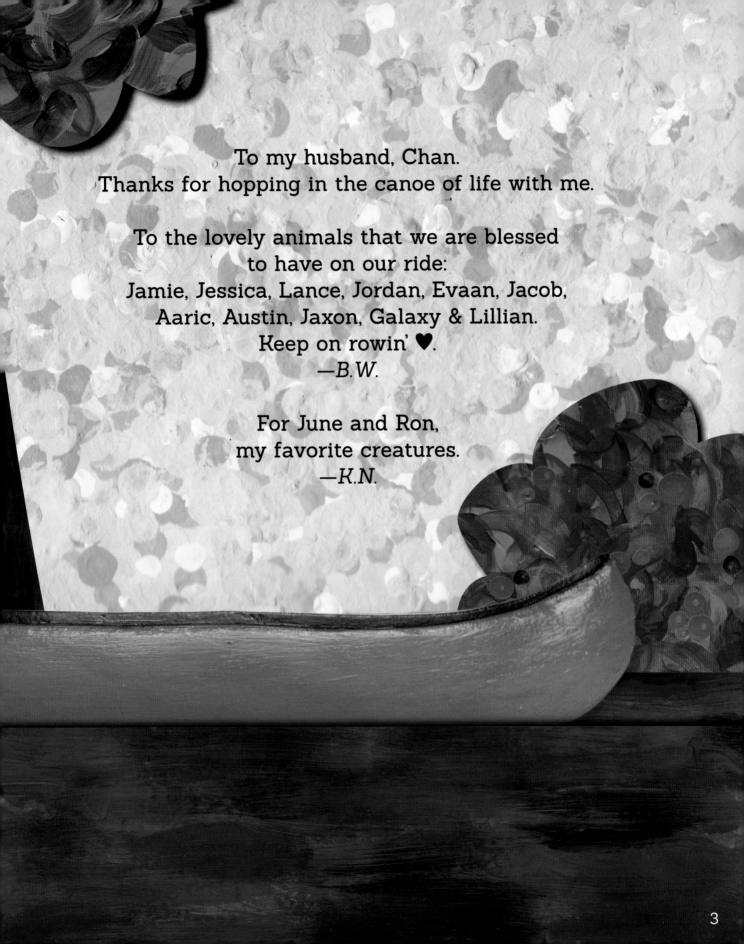

To my husband, Chan.
Thanks for hopping in the canoe of life with me.

To the lovely animals that we are blessed
to have on our ride:
Jamie, Jessica, Lance, Jordan, Evaan, Jacob,
Aaric, Austin, Jaxon, Galaxy & Lillian.
Keep on rowin' ♥.
—*B.W.*

For June and Ron,
my favorite creatures.
—*K.N.*

Rowing down the river
in my canoe, so wide,
I came upon a river toad
and offered him a ride.

"Move over," said the toad.

So I moved over
and off we rowed.

Rowing down the river
in my canoe, so wide,
I came upon a beaver
and offered him a ride.

"Move over," said the beaver.
"Move over," said the toad.

So I moved over
and off we rowed.

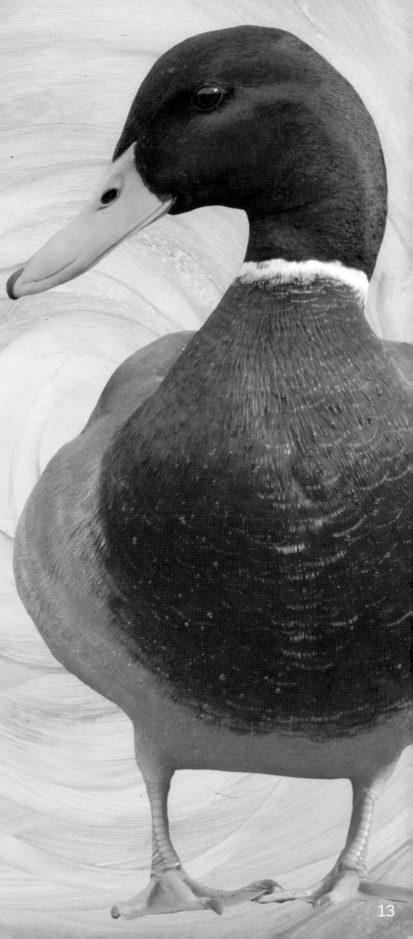

Rowing down
the river,
in my canoe,
so wide,
I came upon
a duck
and offered
him a ride.

"Move over," said the duck,
as he flapped his wings
so he didn't get stuck.
"Move over," said the beaver.
"Move over," said the toad.

So I moved over
and off we rowed.

Rowing down
the river
in my canoe,
so wide,
I came upon
an otter
and offered
him a ride.

"Move over," said the otter.
"Move over," said the duck,
as he flapped his wings
so he didn't get stuck.
"Move over," said the beaver.
"Move over," said the toad.

So I moved over
and off we rowed.

Rowing down the river,
in my canoe, so wide,
I came upon a fish
and offered him a ride.

"Move over," said the fish,
as he flopped his tail
with a swish, swish, swish.
"Move over," said the otter.
"Move over," said the duck,
as he flapped his wings
so he didn't get stuck.
"Move over," said the beaver.
"Move over," said the toad.

So I moved over and off we rowed.

Rowing down
the river,
in my canoe,
so wide,
I came upon
a turtle
and offered
him a ride.

"Move over," said the turtle.
"Move over," said the fish,
as he flopped his tail
with a swish, swish, swish.
"Move over," said the otter.
"Move over," said the duck,
as he flapped his wings
so he didn't get stuck.
"Move over," said the beaver.
"Move over," said the toad.

So I moved over and off we rowed.

Rowing down the river,
in my canoe, so wide,
I came upon an alligator
and FROZE inside.

"Go faster," said the turtle,
"Go faster," said the fish,
as he flopped his tail
with a swish, swish, swish.
"Go faster," said the otter.
"Go faster," said the duck,
as he flapped his wings
so he didn't get stuck.
"Go faster," said the beaver.
"Go faster," said the toad.

So we all worked together,
and off we rowed!

See ya' later, Alligator!

Fresh water sources can be found all over the world. Many animals, including people, count on the clean water of lakes, rivers, ponds, marshes and swamps for survival. Learn more about the animals in this book that call the river "home."

RIVER TOAD

River Toads can be found in the southwest United States and northern Mexico. They spend most of their lives in the desert, but lay eggs in the water and are only tadpoles for a short time. They burrow under the ground for winter. River toads are carnivores (they eat insects and other small animals).

BEAVER

Beavers can be found in North America, Europe and Asia. They are the second largest rodent (part of the rat family) and are mainly nocturnal (sleep during the day). The large front teeth of beavers never stop growing, that is why they love to gnaw on wood. Beavers are herbivores (they eat wood and other plants).

DUCK

Ducks can be found on every continent except for Antarctica. A male duck is called a drake, a female duck is called a hen and a baby duck is called a duckling. They have webbed feet to help them move better under the water. Ducks are omnivores (they eat both plants and small animals or fish).

OTTER

Otters live on every continent except Antarctica and Australia. Otters are very playful creatures and are believed to be one of the few animals that seem to do some activities just for the fun of it. They are often observed sliding down natural waterslides over and over again. Otters are carnivores and eat fish, frogs, crayfish and crabs.

FISH

There are over 32,000 different types of fish and about 40% of those live in freshwater, yet only about 3% of Earth's water is fresh water. Fish have gills that allow them to breathe underwater. Fish are omnivores, eating both plant food and other small animals or insects.

TURTLE

Turtles live in water sources on every continent except Antarctica. They have hard shells for protection. Turtles lay their soft eggs in holes they make in the sand, dirt or grass, then they leave them. They move very slowly, so many people catch them for pets. Turtles are omnivores. They eat insects, plants, fruit and other small animals.

ALLIGATOR

Alligators are found in the southeastern areas of the United States and in China. Chinese alligators live in the Yangtze River and are critically endangered. Alligators have strong jaws and sharp teeth that give them a vicious bite, but the muscles that open the jaw are very weak, therefore a human could hold the jaws of an alligator shut. Alligators are carnivores, eating fish, birds, turtles and even deer or other small animals.